LITERACY FOR AGES 8-9 Ten Minute Tests

CONTENTS

Louis Fidge

Test 1 Verbs

The helicopter **flew** in the sky.

Helicopters **are** flying machines.

Colour in your score on the testometer!

Many verbs are **doing** words. They describe **actions**.

Some verbs are **being** verbs.

Underline the verb in each sentence.

1. A footballer kicks a ball.

2. Some birds catch worms.

3. Caterpillars become butterflies or moths.

4. The car raced along the road.

5. The girl is very scruffy.

6. Mr Patel was late.

7. The train left the station.

8. Aeroplanes land on runways.

9. The mouse ran into the hole.

10. The lady sat in her garden.

11. A baker makes bread.

12. I invited Anna to my party.

13. The worm wriggles away.

14. The children are noisy.

15. The lady showed us the way.

A **phoneme** is the **smallest unit of sound** in a word. A phoneme may be made up of **one or more** letters which make **one sound**.

Colour in your score on the testometer!

b + oy = boy
(two phonemes)

g + ir + l = girl
(three phonemes)

Choose the correct phoneme to complete each word.

1. yesterd_____   (ai/ay)

2. narr_____   (oa/ow)

3. p_____ll   (u/oo)

4. gl_____   (ue/ew)

5. v_____ce   (oy/oi)

6. pr_____l   (ow/ou)

7. str_____   (aw/au)

8. s_____ce   (or/au)

9. cr_____d   (ou/ow)

10. th_____d   (er/ir)

11. sc_____   (are/ere)

12. c_____ly   (er/ur)

13. b_____   (ear/ere)

14. p_____   (ere/air)

15. th_____   (air/ere)

15
14
13
12
11
10
9
8
7
6
5
4
3
2
1

Verbs can be written in different **tenses**.

Now **I am eating** a banana.

Tomorrow **I will eat** a melon.

Yesterday **I ate** an apple.

This happened in the **past**. The verb is in the **past tense**.

This is happening **now**. The verb is in the **present tense**.

This will happen in the **future**. The verb is in the **future tense**.

Colour in your score on the testometer!

Say if the verb in bold is past, present or future tense.

1. I **will go** out to play after tea. _____

2. We **rode** our bikes. _____

3. I **am swimming** in the sea. _____

4. The girl **dropped** her bag in the mud. _____

5. Tomorrow I **will take** my ruler to school. _____

6. I **like** crisps. _____

7. My mum **gave** me some lunch. _____

8. In the summer I **will fly** on a plane. _____

9. I **sleep** in the top bunk. _____

10. My brother **snores**. _____

11. The car **crashed** into a wall. _____

12. Soon the ambulance **will arrive**. _____

13. Next week I **will leave** for Paris. _____

14. Last year I **went** to Spain. _____

15. I **drew** a picture in my book. _____

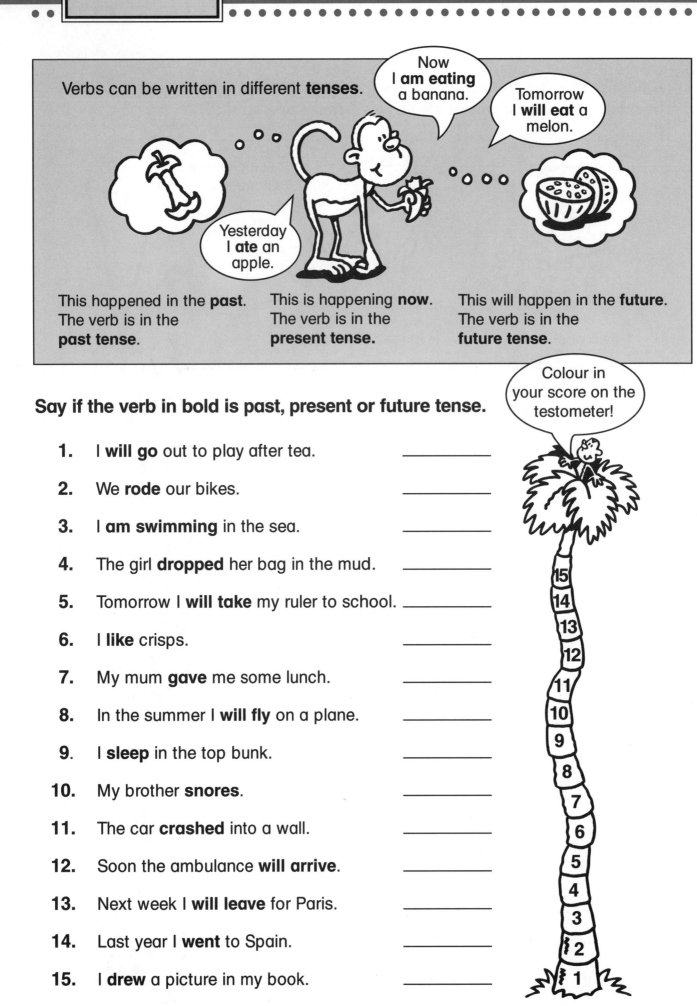

When we say a word slowly, we can hear how it may be broken down into **smaller parts** called **syllables**. Each syllable must contain at least **one vowel**.

Colour in your score on the testometer!

car (one syllable)   ri/ding (two syllables)   car/a/van (three syllables)

Say these words slowly.
Write if they have one, two or three syllables.

1. bike _____

2. scooter _____

3. yesterday _____

4. sun _____

5. afternoon _____

6. summer _____

7. shoes _____

8. dentist _____

9. holiday _____

10. sandwich _____

11. rain _____

12. boat _____

13. syllable _____

14. tonight _____

15. tomorrow _____

A **suffix** is a **group of letters** we add to the **end of a word**.
A suffix changes the **meaning** of a word or the **job the word does**.

paint (verb)   painter (noun)

Colour in your score on the testometer!

Add either the suffix er or or to make these verbs into nouns. Take care with the spelling.

1. bake _____

2. visit _____

3. detect _____

4. clean _____

5. build _____

6. edit _____

7. calculate _____

8. dance _____

9. sail _____

10. print _____

11. radiate _____

12. swim _____

13. inspect _____

14. act _____

15. skate _____

Many reference books are organised in **alphabetical order**.

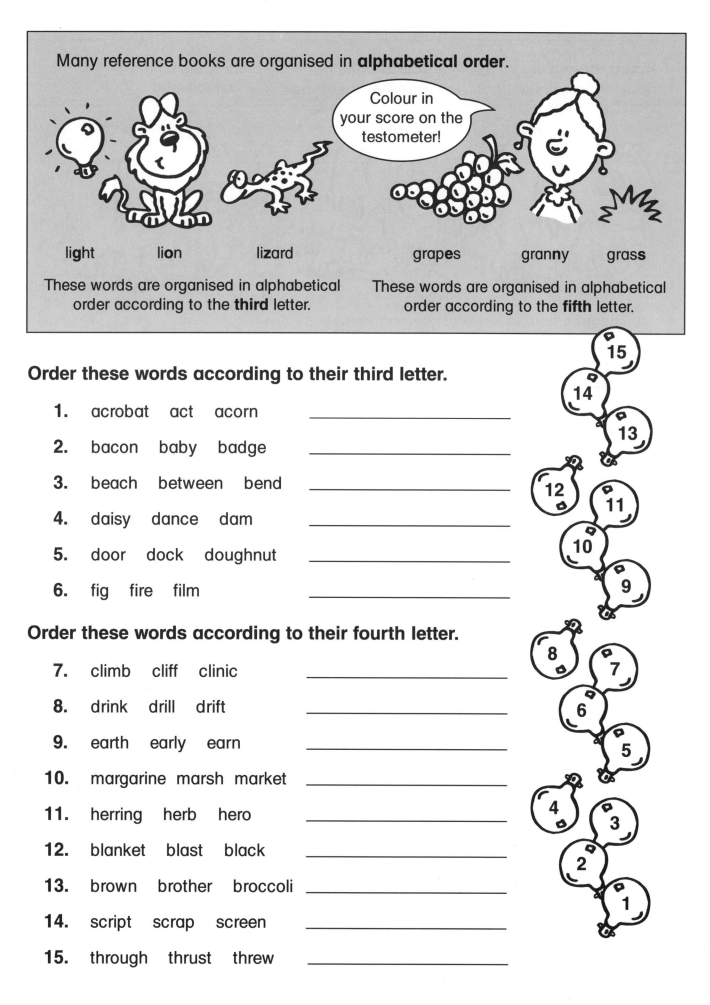

light   lion   lizard

These words are organised in alphabetical order according to the **third** letter.

Colour in your score on the testometer!

grapes   granny   grass

These words are organised in alphabetical order according to the **fifth** letter.

Order these words according to their third letter.

1.   acrobat   act   acorn   _____

2.   bacon   baby   badge   _____

3.   beach   between   bend   _____

4.   daisy   dance   dam   _____

5.   door   dock   doughnut   _____

6.   fig   fire   film   _____

Order these words according to their fourth letter.

7.   climb   cliff   clinic   _____

8.   drink   drill   drift   _____

9.   earth   early   earn   _____

10.   margarine   marsh   market   _____

11.   herring   herb   hero   _____

12.   blanket   blast   black   _____

13.   brown   brother   broccoli   _____

14.   script   scrap   screen   _____

15.   through   thrust   threw   _____

Homophones are words that **sound alike** but have **different spellings** and **different meanings**.

Colour in your score on the testometer!

I **heard** a **herd** of elephants coming towards me.

Choose the correct word to complete each sentence.

1. The _____ shone in the sky.   (sun/son)

2. I _____ my bike.   (rode/road)

3. He ate the _____ cake.   (hole/whole)

4. I had a _____ of pie.   (peace/piece)

5. I tied a _____ in the string.   (not/knot)

6. You have to _____ an apple.   (peal/peel)

7. I measured my _____.   (waste/waist)

8. The man took the quickest _____.   (route/root)

9. The _____ landed at the airport.   (plane/plain)

10. What _____ do you eat for breakfast?   (cereal/serial)

11. It is wrong to _____.   (steal/steel)

12. Bald men have no _____ on their heads. (hairs/hares)

13. The ship had two _____.   (sales/sails)

14. The children took _____ bags.   (there/their)

15. It's easy to get _____.   (board/bored)

15

14

13

12

11

10

9

8

7

6

5

4

3

2

1

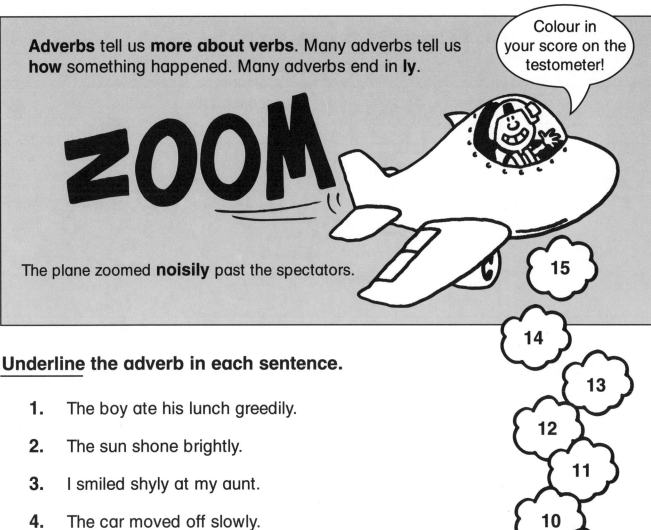

Adverbs tell us **more about verbs**. Many adverbs tell us **how** something happened. Many adverbs end in **ly**.

Colour in your score on the testometer!

The plane zoomed **noisily** past the spectators.

Underline the adverb in each sentence.

1. The boy ate his lunch greedily.

2. The sun shone brightly.

3. I smiled shyly at my aunt.

4. The car moved off slowly.

5. Bravely the knight faced the dragon.

6. The old lady sat down tiredly.

7. Carefully I picked up the model made of matchsticks.

8. The man shouted angrily.

9. Do your work neatly.

10. The thief hurriedly left the shop.

11. Happily I accepted the winner's medal.

12. Are you sitting comfortably?

13. The dog growled fiercely at the stranger.

14. Suddenly it began to rain.

15. I smiled cheerfully.

Look for **smaller words** hidden inside **longer words** to help you to spell them.

Colour in your score on the testometer!

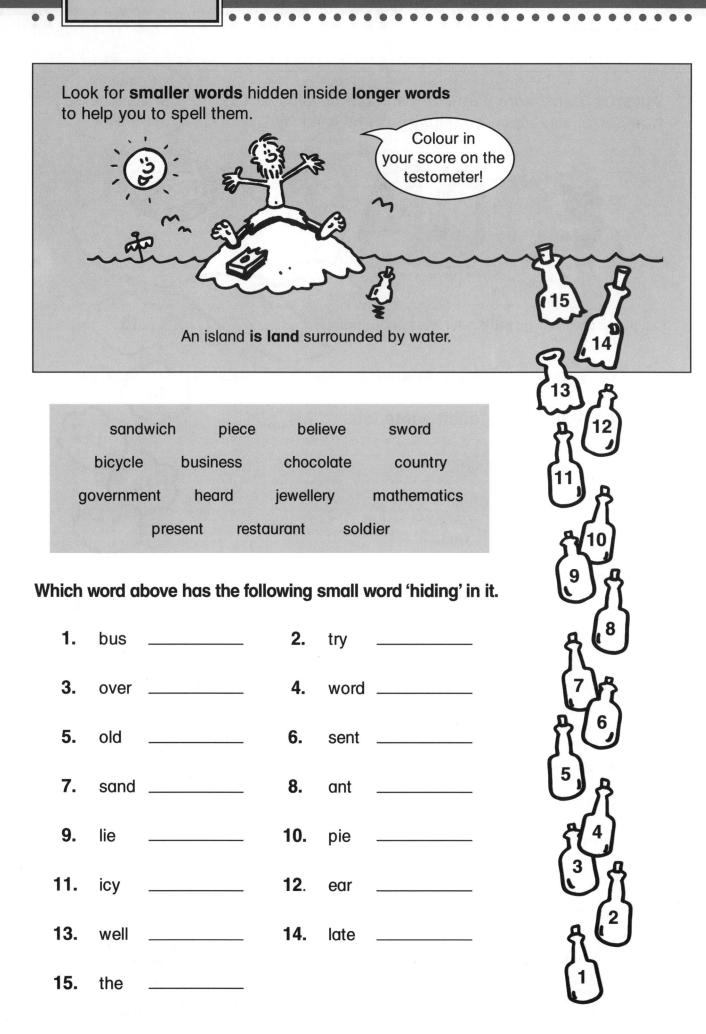

An island **is land** surrounded by water.

sandwich	piece	believe	sword
bicycle	business	chocolate	country
government	heard	jewellery	mathematics
present	restaurant	soldier	

Which word above has the following small word 'hiding' in it.

1. bus _____

2. try _____

3. over _____

4. word _____

5. old _____

6. sent _____

7. sand _____

8. ant _____

9. lie _____

10. pie _____

11. icy _____

12. ear _____

13. well _____

14. late _____

15. the _____

Colour in your score on the testometer!

Ho, Ho!

quick - quickly
We can just add **ly** to many adjectives to make adverbs.

merry - merrily
If the word ends in **y**, we change the **y** to **i** and add **ly**.

miserable - miserably
If the word ends in **e**, we often drop the **e** and add **ly**.

Change these adjectives into adverbs ending in ly.

1. sweet _____

2. hungry _____

3. simple _____

4. plain _____

5. proud _____

6. noble _____

7. idle _____

8. glad _____

9. angry _____

10. feeble _____

11. easy _____

12. willing _____

13. lazy _____

14. possible _____

15. steady _____

An **adjective** is a **describing** word. It gives us more information about the **noun**.

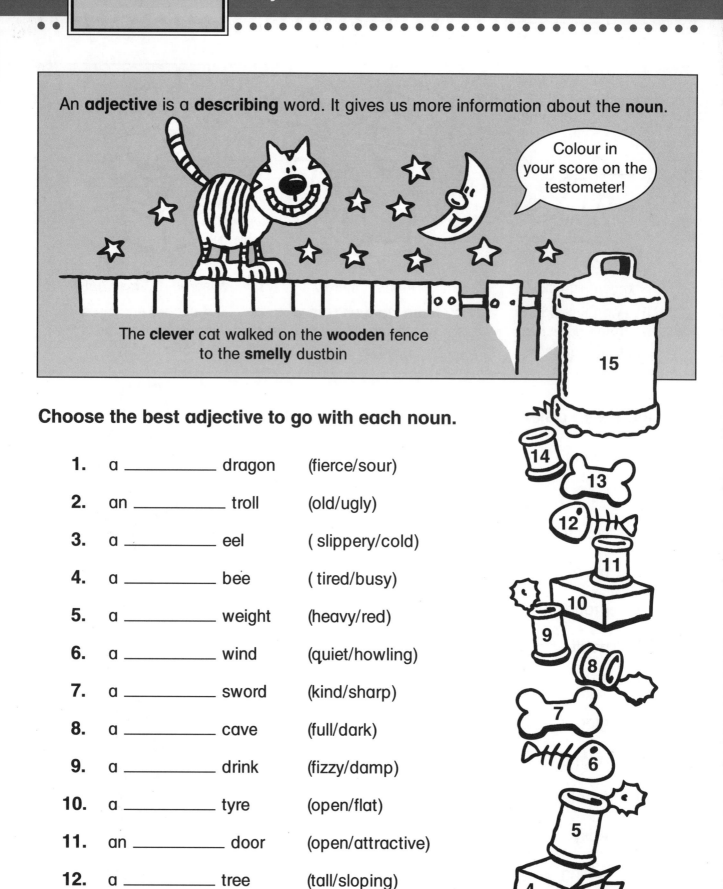

Colour in your score on the testometer!

The **clever** cat walked on the **wooden** fence to the **smelly** dustbin

Choose the best adjective to go with each noun.

1. a _____ dragon   (fierce/sour)

2. an _____ troll   (old/ugly)

3. a _____ eel   (slippery/cold)

4. a _____ bee   (tired/busy)

5. a _____ weight   (heavy/red)

6. a _____ wind   (quiet/howling)

7. a _____ sword   (kind/sharp)

8. a _____ cave   (full/dark)

9. a _____ drink   (fizzy/damp)

10. a _____ tyre   (open/flat)

11. an _____ door   (open/attractive)

12. a _____ tree   (tall/sloping)

13. a _____ sea   (silly/rough)

14. a _____ knife   (blunt/calm)

15. a _____ sheep   (woolly/muddy)

A **simile** is when we **compare** one thing with another.

Colour in your score on the testometer!

He was **as slow as a snail**.

Choose the best adjective to complete each simile.

heavy	black	red	quiet	playful	
	sweet	soft	green	smooth	wise
white	fierce	cool	light	slippery	

1. as _____ as honey

2. as _____ as a kitten

3. as _____ as silk

4. as _____ as butter

5. as _____ as a cucumber

6. as _____ as an owl

7. as _____ as beetroot

8. as _____ as a lion

9 as _____ as grass

10. as _____ as an eel

11. as _____ as snow

12. as _____ as lead

13. as _____ as a feather

14. as _____ as a mouse

15. as _____ as coal

Look for **common letter patterns** to help your spelling.

Colour in your score on the testometer!

catch   switch   hutch

badge	watch	light	dodge	nudge	
	might	sight	fetch	hutch	fight
hedge	bright	stitch	botch	bridge	

Find and write the dge words in alphabetical order.

1._____   2._____   3._____

4._____   5._____

Find and write the tch words in alphabetical order.

6._____   7._____   8._____

9._____   10._____

Find and write the ight words in alphabetical order.

11._____   12._____   13._____

14._____   15._____

When we **compare two nouns** we use a **comparative adjective**.

When we **compare three or more** nouns we use a **superlative adjective**.

Colour in your score on the testometer!

A mouse is **fast**.   A Rabbit is **faster**.   A leopard is the **fastest**.

Fill in the missing adjective. Take care with the spelling.

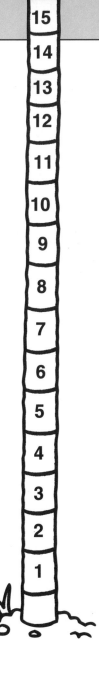

1.	slow	_____	slowest
2.	smooth	smoother	_____
3.	soft	softer	_____
4.	light	_____	lightest
5.	safe	_____	safest
6.	wide	wider	_____
7.	large	larger	_____
8.	wet	_____	wettest
9.	big	bigger	_____
10.	hot	_____	hottest
11.	lucky	_____	luckiest
12.	noisy	noisier	_____
13.	busy	_____	busiest
14.	pretty	_____	prettiest
15.	muddy	muddier	_____

15 14 13 12 11 10 9 8 7 6 5 4 3 2 1

A **suffix** is a **group of letters** we add to the **end** of a word. A suffix changes the **meaning** of the word or the **job** the word does.

magic - magic**al**

Colour in your score on the testometer!

Choose the correct suffix to complete each word.

1. music_____ (al/ous)

2. fashion_____ (able/ible)

3. educa_____ (ment/tion)

4. comic_____ (ment/al)

5. amuse_____ (ous/ment)

6. invis_____ (able/ible)

7. employ_____ (ment/al)

8. inspec_____ (tion/ment)

9. person_____ (tion/al)

10. arrange_____ (tion/ment)

11. comfort_____ (able/ible)

12. entertain_____ (ment/al)

13. sens_____ (able/ible)

14. season_____ (al/ise)

15. ac_____ (ment/tion)

Nouns may be classified according to their **gender**.

a woman
Nouns which refer to
females are **feminine**

a man
Nouns which refer to
males are **masculine**.

Colour in
your score on the
testometer!

Use these nouns to complete the chart below.

princess	grandfather	mother	man	bridegroom
daughter	husband	countess	girl	uncle	king
sister	nephew	headmistress	duke

	masculine	feminine
1.	father	_____
2.	_____	wife
3.	boy	_____
4.	prince	_____
5.	_____	aunt
6.	_____	woman
7.	_____	queen
8.	_____	bride
9.	brother	_____
10.	_____	grandmother
11.	headmaster	_____
12.	_____	niece
13.	count	_____
14.	_____	duchess
15.	son	_____

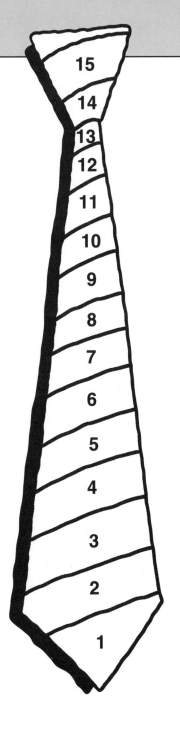

15
14
13
12
11
10
9
8
7
6
5
4
3
2
1

We sometimes **shorten** a word by **leaving out** some letters. These shortened words are called **contractions**. We use an **apostrophe** to show where letters have been left out.

Colour in your score on the testometer!

I'm going on holiday. I'm = I am

Match up each contraction with its longer form.

1.	can't	we have
2.	didn't	do not
3.	we've	can not
4.	you'll	it is
5.	that's	did not
6.	don't	I would
7.	doesn't	shall not
8.	you're	does not
9.	shouldn't	they are
10.	we'll	you will
11.	I'd	will not
12.	it's	should not
13.	they're	we will
14.	shan't	that is
15.	won't	you are

Colour in your score on the testometer!

Long ago, dinosaurs roamed the earth.
Commas are used to separate **extra bits** that are **added** to sentences.

The car, a red one, was parked outside the shop.
Commas help to **break up** longer sentences **into smaller parts**.

Put the missing commas in each of these sentences.

1. That boy the smaller one shouted rude names at me.

2. Don't do that Sam!

3. Pass me my cup of tea please.

4. Feeling rather tired Goldilocks sat down on the chair.

5. Let's go out shall we?

6. Whenever I can I like to go out.

7. Pick up your bag Anna.

8. The dog a spotted Dalmatian escaped from the garden.

9. If I can find one I always buy a comic.

10. Quiet please!

11. No I don't want a sandwich.

12. Whether it's rugby or football I enjoy the game.

13. What's the matter Mrs Shah?

14. Once upon a time there lived an ugly troll.

15. That's very nice thank you.

NO PARKING

15
14
13
12
11
10
9
8
7
6
5
4
3
2
1

Sometimes when we **change the order** of words, it **changes the meaning** of the sentence.

Colour in your score on the testometer!

The dog chased the postman.   The postman chased the dog.

Rearrange the words in these sentences so they make sense.

1. The sandwich ate a man. _____

2. The car got into the prince. _____

3. The crown put on his king. _____

4. The laugh made us clown. _____

5. The tree climbed the squirrel. _____

6. The piano played the teacher. _____

7. The trunk lifted its elephant. _____

8. The ball kicked a footballer. _____

9. Some boots wore children. _____

10. The runway landed on the plane. _____

11. An egg fried the girl. _____

12. The bone picked up the dog. _____

13. The television is watching Sam. _____

14. A tunnel went through the train. _____

15. Stripes have tigers. _____

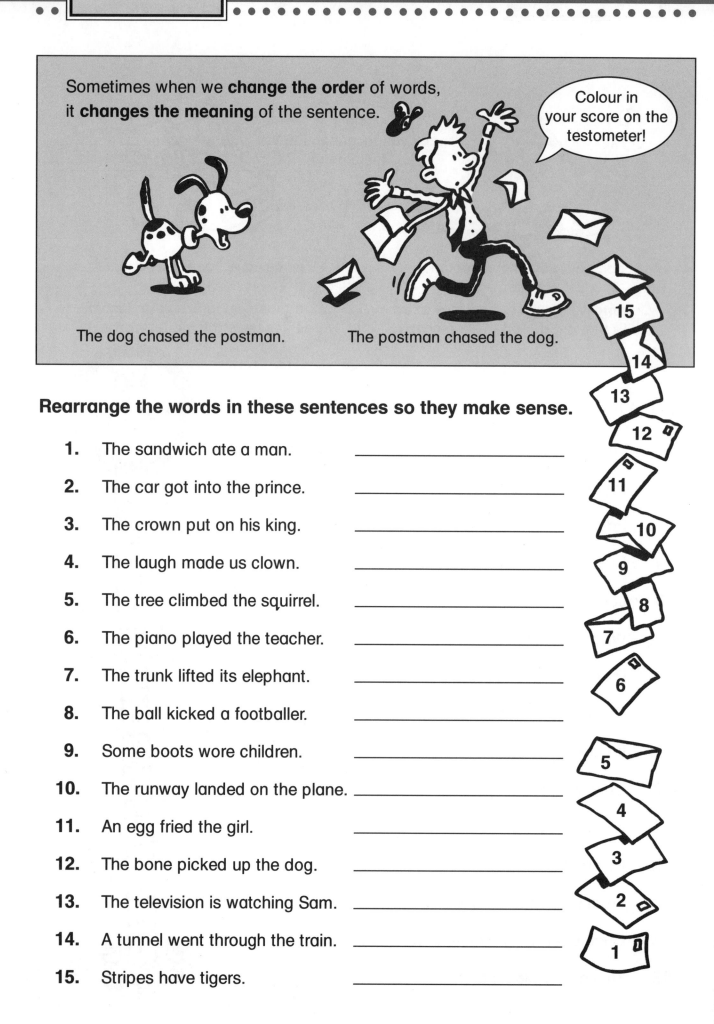

×28

We use an **apostrophe** to show **ownership** (that something belongs to someone).

When there is **only one** owner, we usually write **'s**.

When there is **more than one** owner, we usually write **s'**.

Colour in your score on the testometer!

the boy's books
(the books belong to one boy)

the boys' books
(the books belong to more than one boy)

Write the shortened form of each phrase.

1. the bike belongs to the girl   the girl's bike

2. the pen belongs to the boy   _____

3. the car belongs to the man   _____

4. the cup belongs to my brother   _____

5. the nuts belong to the squirrels   _____

6. the ship belongs to the sailors   _____

7. the school belongs to the teachers   _____

8. the tie belongs to Sam   _____

9. the bag belongs to Dr Smith   _____

10. the cubs belong to the lion   _____

11. the bananas belong to the monkeys   _____

12. the ball belongs to the footballers   _____

13. the guitar belongs to the singer   _____

14. the barn belongs to the farmer   _____

15. the hose belongs to the fire-fighters   _____

A **compound word** is made up of **two smaller words** joined together.

Colour in your score on the testometer!

cup + board = cupboard

Write these compound words as two separate words.

1. passport _____ _____

2. birthday _____ _____

3. overseas _____ _____

4. broadcast _____ _____

5. driftwood _____ _____

6. rainforest _____ _____

7. courtyard _____ _____

8. trapdoor _____ _____

9. horseback _____ _____

10. underground _____ _____

11. stairway _____ _____

12. cloakroom _____ _____

13. roundabout _____ _____

14. keyhole _____ _____

15. breakfast _____ _____

15
14
13
12
11
10
9
8
7
6
5
4
3
2
1

Diminutives are words that imply something **small**.

duck – duckling

A **diminutive** can sometimes be made by adding a **suffix**.

frog – tadpole

A **diminutive** can sometimes be a **different word altogether**.

Colour in your score on the testometer!

Match up each noun with its correct diminutive.

1.	owl	fawn
2.	bear	eaglet
3.	deer	owlet
4.	goose	chick
5.	cow	cub
6.	swan	lambkin
7.	bull	puppy
8.	eagle	gosling
9.	dog	grub
10.	hen	kitten
11.	horse	calf
12.	lamb	tadpole
13.	cat	bullock
14.	frog	foal
15.	wasp	cygnet

Letters do not always sound the way we expect them to.

Colour in your score on the testometer!

wash
When **a** comes after **w** it often sounds like **o**.

swarm
When **ar** comes after **w** it often sounds like **or**.

worm
When **or** comes after **w** it often sounds like **er**.

Choose a, ar or or to complete each word.

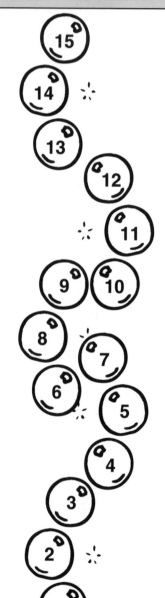

1. w_____sh

2. wh_____f

3. w_____ld

4. w_____th

5. sw_____m

6. w_____ddle

7. w_____nder

8. dw_____f

9. w_____tch

10. w_____se

11. w_____rant

12. w_____p

13. w_____k

14. w_____thy

15. w_____llet

There are **four** different **types of sentences**.

What colour is your car?

My car is silver.

Wash my car, please.

What a lovely car!

A **question** asks something.

A **statement** gives information.

A **command** tells someone to do something.

An **exclamation** shows someone feels strongly about something.

Write what type of sentence each of these is.

1. The door is shut. _____

2. Where is my bag? _____

3. Go and have a bath. _____

4. What a muddy T-shirt! _____

5. When are you going? _____

6. It's not fair! _____

7. I'm going to bed. _____

8. Turn off the television. _____

9. I think that's wonderful! _____

10. How did you get lost? _____

11. Tom likes tennis. _____

12. Cut the paper with scissors. _____

13. Put the kettle on. _____

14. Help! _____

15. Who are you going with? _____

Colour in your score on the testometer!

15
14
13
12
11
10
9
8
7
6
5
4
3
2
1

We can add the suffixes **ing** and **ed** to many verbs.

talk

talking

Colour in your score on the testometer!

talk – talking – talked

15
14
13
12
11
10
9
8
7
6
5
4
3
2
1

Add the suffix ing **to these verbs. Take care! Sometimes you may have to change the spelling of the root verb.**

1. look _____

2. tap _____

3. make _____

4. shrug _____

5. hop _____

6. shout _____

7. use _____

8. carry _____

Add the suffix ed **to these verbs. Take care! Sometimes you may have to change the spelling of the root verb.**

9. pin _____

10. try _____

11. marry _____

12. slip _____

13. fade _____

14. hope _____

15. walk _____

The two common word endings **tion** and **sion** sometimes get confused.

Please come to my party RSVP

Colour in your score on the testometer!

invita**tion**

The **tion** at the end of words sounds like **shun**.

televi**sion**

The **sion** at the end of words sounds like **zhon**.

**The ending of each of these words is wrong.
Write each word correctly.**

1. conversasion _____
2. explotion _____
3. sucsion _____
4. invation _____
5. confution _____
6. preparasion _____
7. creasion _____
8. revition _____
9. competision _____
10. populasion _____
11. divition _____
12. composision _____
13. conclution _____
14. inclution _____
15. fracsion _____

The two common word endings **able** and **ible** sometimes get confused.

Colour in your score on the testometer!

comfort + able = comfortable

It is often possible to see the root word when **able** is added.

horror + ible = horrible

It is **not** often possible to see the root word when **ible** is added.

Choose able **or** ible **to complete each word.**

1. poss_____

2. reason_____

3. terr_____

4. reli_____

5. fashion_____

6. flex_____

7. remark_____

8. suit_____

9. respons_____

10. revers_____

11. sens_____

12. valu_____

13. miser_____

14. favour_____

15. vis_____

Test 28 | Common letter strings

Some **letter strings** are very **common** – but they do not always make the same sound.

Colour in your score on the testometer!

match ☑   watch ☐   catch ☑

Underline the odd word out in each set.

1.   tough   cough   rough

2.   five   hive   give

3.   have   wave   gave

4.   lost   cost   post

5.   how   glow   now

6.   love   glove   move

7.   height   eight   weight

8.   though   dough   trough

9.   bear   near   fear

10.   good   hood   blood

11.   vase   case   base

12.   cough   trough   through

13.   stone   gone   bone

14.   caught   daughter   laugh

15.   wallet   mallet   pallet

A **conjunction** is a **joining** word. It may be used to join two sentences.

SHOP

Colour in your score on the testometer!

The car was speeding. It passed the shop.

(two sentences)

The car was speeding **as** It passed the shop.

(one sentence with a conjunction)

Find and <u>underline</u> the conjunction in each sentence.

1. It rained heavily but we carried on with the game.

2. The teacher opened the door and the children came in.

3. I went to the shop but it was closed.

4. The children went outside and played in the garden.

5. The monkey will not come unless you give it a banana.

6. He was given the prize because he deserved it.

7. I got lost when I drove through the town.

8. I gave her another sweet as she had eaten the last one.

9. He bought me the present although he couldn't afford it.

10. Do not climb the tree or you might fall.

11. You will not pass the test if you don't try harder.

12. I went indoors when it began raining.

13. The girl will not go to school unless her mother brings her.

14. We started early so we would finish in time for tea.

15. I was nervous as I hadn't seen my uncle for a long time.

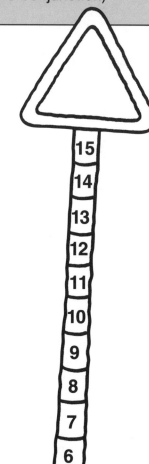

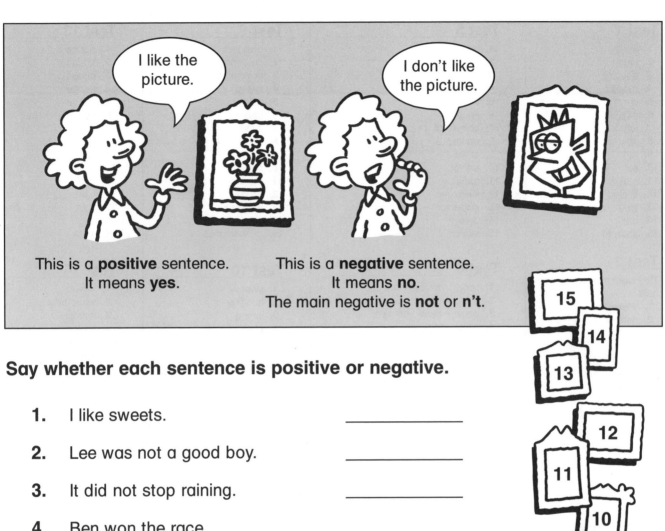

This is a **positive** sentence.
It means **yes**.

This is a **negative** sentence.
It means **no**.
The main negative is **not** or **n't**.

Say whether each sentence is positive or negative.

1.   I like sweets. _____

2.   Lee was not a good boy. _____

3.   It did not stop raining. _____

4.   Ben won the race. _____

5.   I didn't do my homework last night. _____

6.   You should always smile. _____

7.   You should never tell lies. _____

8.   My drawing is nice. _____

9.   I don't like spelling. _____

10. I hate maths. _____

11. Don't shout. _____

12. You must not run. _____

13. The old lady could not lift the box. _____

14. I can't whistle. _____

15. I can knit. _____

Answers

Test 1
1. kicks
2. catch
3. become
4. raced
5. is
6. was
7. left
8. land
9. ran
10. sat
11. makes
12. invited
13. wriggles
14. are
15. showed

Test 2
The correct phoneme is in **bold**.
1. yesterd**ay**
2. na**rrow**
3. p**u**ll
4. gl**ue**
5. v**oi**ce
6. pr**ow**l
7. str**aw**
8. s**au**ce
9. cr**ow**d
10. th**ir**d
11. sc**are**
12. c**ur**ly
13. b**ear**
14. p**air**
15. th**ere**

Test 3
1. future
2. past
3. present
4. past
5. future
6. present
7. past
8. future
9. present
10. present
11. past
12. future
13. future
14. past
15. past

Test 4
1. one
2. two
3. three
4. one
5. three
6. two
7. one
8. two
9. three
10. two
11. one
12. one
13. three
14. two
15. three

Test 5
1. baker
2. visitor
3. detector
4. cleaner
5. builder
6. editor
7. calculator
8. dancer
9. sailor
10. printer
11. radiator
12. swimmer
13. inspector
14. actor
15. skater

Test 6
1. acorn acrobat act
2. baby bacon badge
3. beach bend between
4. daisy dam dance
5. dock door doughnut
6. fig film fire
7. cliff climb clinic
8. drift drill drink
9. early earn earth
10. margarine market marsh
11. herb hero herring
12. black blanket blast
13. broccoli brother brown
14. scrap screen script
15. threw through thrust

Test 7
1. sun
2. rode
3. whole
4. piece
5. knot
6. peel
7. waist
8. route
9. plane
10. cereal
11. steal
12. hairs
13. sails
14. their
15. bored

Test 8
1. greedily
2. brightly
3. shyly
4. slowly
5. Bravely
6. tiredly
7. Carefully
8. angrily
9. neatly
10. hurriedly
11. Happily
12. comfortably
13. fiercely
14. Suddenly
15. cheerfully

Test 9
1. business
2. country
3. government
4. sword
5. soldier
6. present
7. sandwich
8. restaurant
9. believe
10. piece
11. bicycle
12. heard
13. jewellery
14. chocolate
15. mathematics

Test 10
1. sweetly
2. hungrily
3. simply
4. plainly
5. proudly
6. nobly
7. idly
8. gladly
9. angrily
10. feebly
11. easily
12. willingly
13. lazily
14. possibly
15. steadily

Test 11
1. fierce
2. ugly
3. slippery
4. busy
5. heavy
6. howling
7. sharp
8. dark
9. fizzy
10. flat
11. open
12. tall
13. rough
14. blunt
15. woolly

Test 12
1. sweet
2. playful
3. smooth
4. soft
5. cool
6. wise
7. red
8. fierce
9. green
10. slippery
11. white
12. heavy
13. light
14. quiet
15. black

Test 13
1. badge
2. bridge
3. dodge
4. hedge
5. nudge
6. botch
7. fetch
8. hutch
9. stitch
10. watch
11. bright
12. fight
13. light
14. might
15. sight

Test 14
1. slower
2. smoothest
3. softest
4. lighter
5. safer
6. widest
7. largest
8. wetter
9. biggest
10. hotter
11. luckier
12. noisiest
13. busier
14. prettier
15. muddiest

Test 15
The correct suffix is in **bold**.
1. music**al**
2. fashion**able**
3. educat**ion**
4. comic**al**
5. amuse**ment**
6. invis**ible**
7. employ**ment**
8. inspec**tion**
9. person**al**
10. arrange**ment**
11. comfort**able**
12. entertain**ment**
13. sens**ible**
14. season**al**
15. ac**tion**

Test 16
1. mother
2. husband
3. girl
4. princess
5. uncle
6. man
7. king
8. bridegroom
9. sister
10. grandfather
11. headmistress
12. nephew
13. countess
14. duke
15. daughter